THE GIRL WHO WOULD BE KING

AND OTHER ROMANIAN FAIRY TALES

PETRE ISPIRESCU

Translated by

ALEXA J ISPAS

ISBN: 978-1-913926-08-3 (ebk)

ISBN: 978-1-913926-10-6 (pbk)

CONTENTS

INTRODUCTION

WRITTEN BY ALEXA J ISPAS (TRANSLATOR)

The stories in this book are old...How old, no one knows.

They were being told among Romanian people in the 19th century while they were sitting by the fire, after long days working the field.

These stories, and all the others in the *Romanian Stories* series, are remarkable.

They address universal human themes that are relevant to us today, yet also provide a glimpse into a way of life different from our own.

Petre Ispirescu, a young man born in 1830 who had grown up around Romanian fairy tales and had trained at a publishing house, decided to start collecting these stories and publish them.

His first published collection dates from 1862, and he continued publishing these stories until close to his death, two decades later.

A couple of these stories are part of the literature curriculum in Romanian schools, which is how I first came across them.

Yet many of them are unknown to most Romanian people.

They had certainly been unknown to me, until I accidentally stumbled upon *Ileana Samziana* a while ago, many years after having moved from my native Romania to start a new life in the UK.

That story, which I re-titled *The Girl Who Would Be King* in my translated version, felt like a revelation.

Here was a transgender story, published in a 19th century Romanian book of fairy tales!

Petre Ispirescu's collection had many more surprises in store for me, as I started reading my way through the rest of his tales.

I loved these stories so much that I decided to translate and adapt them for an English-speaking, contemporary audience, and publish them as a series of short, easy-to-read books.

In doing so, I did my best to stay true to the narrative heart of each story, yet filter out elements of racial discrimination and other such aspects that do not sit well with my 21st century values.

I have also taken creative license with many of the titles, as well as the sentence structure and length.

Following each tale, I have included a *Translator's Note* in which I summarize the changes I have made, for any readers who would like to know more about how my translated and adapted version differs from the original.

I have also used that section to add short pieces of personal commentary focused on various aspects of the story, as well as to point readers to related tales or other relevant resources that may be of interest.

This type of direct message from the translator to the reader is rather unusual in translated works, but I hope that readers will enjoy the transparency and added insight these sections provide.

As such, the books in the *Romanian Stories* series also represent an experiment in the art of putting together a translated version of a piece of work.

The book you are currently reading contains four of the tales collected by Petre Ispirescu.

If you enjoy these stories, you can find more at www.storybothy.com

THE GIRL WHO WOULD BE KING

Once upon a time, there was strong and mighty king.

He had won battles against his neighboring kings and had made them obey him.

In this way, he had expanded the boundaries of his kingdom.

As part of the peace agreement, the defeated kings were ordered to send to him one of their sons to serve him for ten years.

For a long time, one king had successfully defended his country against the all-powerful king.

But as he had reached old age, he too had been forced to enter into an agreement with the all-powerful king, as he could no longer lead his army to victory.

The trouble was, he could not send one of his sons to serve the all-powerful king, because he only had three daughters.

What was going to happen, if he did not comply?

Was the all-powerful king going to take his kingdom away?

He worried that if he incurred the all-powerful king's wrath and lost his kingdom, he and his daughters would have to live out the rest of their days in poverty and shame.

The three daughters, seeing their father increasingly plagued by worry, started wondering what was causing it.

They did not know what to do to cheer him up.

When they saw that nothing was to his liking, the eldest daughter brought up the courage to ask him one day, at dinner time, what was worrying him.

"Does our behavior displease you?" she asked. "Are the servants badly behaved? Tell us, dad, what is disturbing your peace and poisoning your old age? We promise to do whatever is needed to relieve your sadness."

"You, my dears, cannot quell the pain that is seeping into my soul. Only a son could take me out of the sea of problems I am finding myself in."

"I don't understand," the eldest daughter said. "Why are you hiding from us the source of your worries?"

"My dears," the king said, "as long as you have been on this earth, you have busied yourselves with the needle and the weaving loom. You know how to spin, to sew, to weave. Only a hero could save me, someone who knows how to handle a mace, to carry a sword with courage, and to ride like a dragon."

"Tell us anyway, father. We want to know what is worrying you."

As the girls persisted with their pleas, the king said:

"Here is the reason, my daughters, for my sadness. You know that no one has been able to touch my kingdom for as long as I was young without getting their due reward and returning to wherever they had come from in shame. Now though, old age has drained me of my powers. My arms are weak. They can no longer handle the sword or make the enemy tremble. My horse, who has helped me win every battle in my younger days, is also old. He is full of disease, and barely drags himself around, living from day to day. In previous times, I was able to strike fear into my enemies. But nowadays, what can I say? You know that I have agreed to obey the powerful king. But with him, the custom is that all those under his power send him a son to serve him for ten years, and I only have you."

"I will go, father," said the eldest daughter, "and I will do my best to please you."

"I fear you will return not having accomplished anything. Who knows in what trouble you will get yourself there, that no one will be able to untangle?"

"All I know, father, and what I can promise, is that I will not embarrass you."

"If this is how it is, get ready and go."

As soon as the girl obtained her father's permission, she was beside herself with joy and started getting ready.

She was on her feet all day long, giving orders and packing all the things she needed for the journey.

She chose the most majestic horse from the

royal stables, the most beautiful and expensive clothes, and packed enough food for an entire year.

When her father saw that she was ready to leave, he advised her on how she should act so no one would realize she was a girl.

He taught her everything a hero who is about to take on a high-ranking job would need to know.

He also taught her how to avoid gossip, and how to fit in with the sons of the other kings.

Then, he said to her:

"May God take you in His care. Remember what I have taught you."

The girl set off as quickly as lightning.

The entire earth could not contain her happiness.

If she hadn't at some point stopped to wait for her servants and her food supplies, these would have gotten lost, because they could not keep up with her.

Meanwhile, the king set off on a side path that led towards the edges of his kingdom and stopped by a road she would have to pass through.

There he put up a bridge made of copper,

transformed himself into a wolf, and hid underneath the bridge.

When the girl was about to pass, the wolf suddenly jumped out at her, baring his teeth.

He looked so frightening, he would have put the fear of death into anyone.

His eyes shone like flames as he looked straight into hers, and he seemed ready to gorge her.

The girl froze with fear and lost her nerve.

If the horse had not jumped to the side, the wolf would have stuck his claws into her.

She galloped back to her father's kingdom at great speed.

Her father, who used the side path to return before she did, came out to welcome her back.

"Did I not tell you, my dear, that not all flies make honey?" he said.

"That is true, father, but I did not know that going to serve a king meant I would have to fight such wild and rabid beasts."

"If this is how it is," said the king, "stay at home and take care of your spindle and your spools. May God have mercy on me, and not let me die in shame."

Not long passed and the second daughter also asked to go.

She promised that she would do everything in her power to carry out the task she had set herself right through to the end.

After much pleading and many promises, her father relented and allowed her to go.

But the same thing happened to her as had happened to her older sister.

Welcoming her back, her father said:

"Well, my daughter, did I not tell you that not all flies make honey?"

"That's true, father, that's what you said. But that wolf was just too scary. He opened his maw to devour me, and looked at me with eyes that seemed to pierce through my soul."

"So stay home," the king said, "and take care of the broomsticks and the vegetables in the kitchen."

Time passed.

Then one day, as they were having dinner, the youngest daughter said to her father:

"Father, let me try my luck as well."

"Given that your older sisters have not been able to carry out their plan, I wonder how you even think to put yourself forward," the king said.

"You have barely figured out how to eat out of a bowl."

He tried to curtail her wish to go in all sorts of ways, but in vain.

"For the love of you, dad," she said, "I will work like four devils to succeed. But if God bars my way, I will return to you without shame."

Her father kept trying to dissuade her and was reluctant to let her go, but his daughter persuaded him with her pleas.

Eventually, the king said:

"If you really want to go, I will give you permission. Let me see what you end up doing. How I will laugh if I see you return with your nose to the ground."

"You will laugh, dad, as you have laughed at my sisters too, without this diminishing their honor."

Having gained her father's permission, the king's youngest daughter went to the royal stables, where the best stallions in the entire kingdom were kept, to choose herself a horse.

She examined one horse, then another, but none of them caught her eye.

After much searching, she found her father's old horse, the one he had ridden since his youth.

The horse was lying on his side, full of disease and scabs.

As soon as she saw him, she was overcome by pity and could not bear to leave his side.

The horse said:

"I can see that because of the love you have for the king, you are looking at me like this. What a hero he was in his youth! The two of us have been through many adventures together. But since he has grown old, he has stopped taking me out for a ride. And I am skinny like this because there is nobody who can feed me like he can. If someone were to take care of me the way he did, in ten days I would become as strong as ten of the other royal horses."

"How would you need to be taken care of?" the girl asked.

"I would need to be washed every day with pure water, to be given barley boiled in sweet milk, and be fed a bushel of hot embers."

"If I could be sure you will help me reach my goal, I would be tempted to do as you say."

"Mistress," the horse said, "I promise you will not regret it."

The king's daughter took care of him just as he had taught her to do.

On the tenth day, he shook himself three times and became beautiful, as plump as a melon and as limber as a deer.

Then, looking happily at the king's daughter, he said:

"May God give you luck and success, mistress. You have cared for me and allowed me to once again be the way I wanted to be in this world. Tell me what you want me to do."

"I want to go to the big and mighty king, our neighbor, to serve him, and I need someone to advise me along the way."

"If you will go with me," the horse told her, "I will serve you the way I have served your father, as long as you follow my advice."

"In that case, we will leave in three days."

The king's daughter started making preparations for the journey.

She took some clean clothes, but without frills, a few food items, and some spending money.

As her father came to say his goodbyes, she said:

"May God be with you, dad, and may I find you in good health."

"Have a good trip, my daughter," her father

said. "Just don't forget what I have taught you. And whenever you are in need, focus your mind on God, the source of all that is good and of all help."

After she promised to do so, the girl set off.

As with his other two daughters, the king took a shortcut and overtook her.

He set up the copper bridge, transformed into a wolf, and waited for her while hiding underneath the bridge.

On the way, the horse told the girl that her father was going to test her bravery.

He advised her on what to do to pass the test.

When they arrived at the bridge, the wolf jumped towards her.

His eyes flashed and his fangs were bared, to put the fear of death into her.

He looked ravenous, as if he hadn't eaten for a month.

But when the beast was about to dig his claws in, the girl gave the horse a signal.

She charged against the wolf holding her sword, ready to tear him to pieces.

If the wolf hadn't jumped to the side, she would have cut him in two.

She had decided that no matter what, she would fulfill the task she had taken upon herself.

She passed over the bridge as triumphant as any male hero.

Her father marveled at her courage.

Then he took another shortcut, overtook her again, set up a bridge made of silver, transformed himself into a lion, and waited for her underneath the bridge.

The horse, however, had already warned the girl about what she was about to encounter.

He had also taught her how to overcome this second test.

As soon as the girl reached the silver bridge, the lion jumped at her with his maw wide open.

He seemed ready to devour her and her horse, with fangs like ivory and claws like scythes, and roaring so loudly that the forest shook and the earth rumbled.

Looking at his head as large as an ox and his mane upright and disheveled, anyone would have been overcome with fear.

But the king's daughter, encouraged by the horse, charged against him with her sword, ready to strike.

If the lion had not run back to his hiding

place underneath the bridge, he would have been quartered.

Then she passed over the bridge, thanking God and getting herself ready for the next challenge.

Having never left home before, she was full of wonder seeing the beauty of the fields.

She would have liked to get off the horse to gather a bunch of the beautiful flowers that were covering the valleys and hills, flowers she had never seen before.

Or to stand in the shadow of a tall and bushy tree, in which thousands of birds were singing songs so sweet, they could have sung anyone to sleep.

And over on the other side she would have liked to go to the small river with water as clear as tears, which had sprung from the corner of some rock from the side of the hills.

She was looking at the river with longing, enjoying its sounds and watching as the water meandered along the earth, surrounded by flowers and the greenery of spring.

But the horse was pushing her to keep going.

"Young men do not take a look at these things

until after they have completed their task," he kept telling her.

He also warned her that her father had set yet another trap for her, and taught her how to emerge victorious once more.

The girl was listening to her horse's advice and following it to the letter.

She had seen that it had led to good things, and she did not waver in her obedience.

Her father, as before, took a shortcut and overtook her.

He set up a bridge made of gold, transformed himself into a twelve-headed dragon and hid himself underneath the bridge.

When the girl was about to pass over the bridge, she was suddenly confronted by an enormous dragon with twelve heads, smashing his tail against the ground.

Fire was gushing from his twelve mouths, and his twelve tongues looked like burning arrows.

When the girl saw how frightening the dragon looked, her hair stood on edge.

The horse, sensing that she was about to lose her nerve, reminded her what he had taught her, and she found a small bit of courage within herself.

She held on to his harness and spurred him on as she charged against the dragon with her sword.

The battle lasted a whole hour.

The horse was telling her when to go to the side to cut off one of the dragon's heads, but the enemy was guarding himself pretty well.

In the end, the girl succeeded in wounding the dragon.

At that point, with three summersaults, he turned human again.

The girl could not believe her eyes when she saw her father before her.

And he, taking her in his arms and kissing her forehead, said:

"I see that you are brave, my daughter. You have done well to pick this horse, because without him you would have returned home the same as your sisters. I hope that you will bring the task which you have taken upon yourself to a good end. Remember what I have taught you and always follow your horse's advice."

Then they parted ways.

After going for a long time, they reached some big mountains.

Between the mountains they came across two *zmei*, fearsome human-like creatures with magic powers, who had been fighting for nine years.

Neither of the *zmei* had been able to prove himself the strongest, nor was either of them prepared to relent, as they were fighting to kill.

When they saw the king's daughter, thinking she was a young man, one of the *zmei* said:

"Prince Charming, help me slay this enemy of mine, and I will one day be of service to you too."

The other one said:

"Prince Charming, help me slay this enemy of mine, and I will give you 'Yellow Sun', my fearless horse."

The girl asked the horse whom of the two *zmei* she should help.

The horse said to rescue the one who had promised to give her Yellow Sun, because he is his younger brother and even more fearless.

So the girl charged against the other *zmeu* with her sword and cut off his head with one strike.

The surviving *zmeu* hugged his savior and thanked her.

Then he invited her home so he could give her Yellow Sun, as he had promised.

The *zmeu*'s mother could not contain her happiness when she saw her son.

She did not know how to thank Prince Charming for having saved her son's life.

"I would like to rest after my long journey," the king's daughter said, so they offered her a room and left her alone.

The girl went to the stables to tend to her horse and ask him if she should be wary of anything.

The horse told her what to expect and how she should respond.

Meanwhile, the *zmeu*'s mother suspected that there was something odd going on.

She told her son that the young lad who had saved him from danger was in fact a girl, and that she would make a perfect wife for him.

But her son did not believe her.

He thought no female could have handled a sword as well as his rescuer had done.

The *zmeu*'s mother decided to prove to her son that her suspicion was correct.

That evening, she placed a bundle of flowers at each of their heads.

At whose head the flowers were to welt, that one was a man.

If, on the other hand, the flowers would remain green, the sleeper was a woman.

Following the horse's advice, the king's daughter made sure to rise towards dawn, when the sleep was sweetest.

Walking gingerly on her tiptoes, she went into the *zmeu*'s room.

She put her own bundle of flowers at his head, took his, and returned to her room where she put it at her head before going back to sleep.

In the morning, when the *zmeu*'s mother woke up, she immediately went to her son's room.

There she found the flowers to be wilted, as she had expected.

After the king's daughter woke up, the *zmeu*'s mother went to her room as well, where she expected to find the flowers still green and fresh.

But even after seeing that these flowers had wilted as well, she still couldn't believe that her son's rescuer was a lad.

She told her son that Prince Charming could not be male.

The words were flowing out of his mouth like honey, his face was so sweet you wanted to soak it in, his hair was falling on his shoulders in waves, his hands and feet were as small and delicate as an elf's, and his face seemed to say 'come hither' with big, beautiful eyes so alive they made you dizzy.

All of these things could only belong to a girl, even though she was hiding herself under a lad's clothes.

To prove her suspicion, the *zmeu*'s mother decided to try one other thing, and taught her son what to do.

After they said good morning to each other, the *zmeu* invited his rescuer to accompany him into the garden.

There, the *zmeu* showed the king's daughter all the different kinds of flowers that were growing there and invited her to sample their sweet scent.

But the king's daughter remembered her horse's advice and recognized this as another test.

"Why did you bring me into the garden like a woman to admire the flowers?" she said in an assertive voice. "We should go to the stables to see how the horses are being cared for."

The *zmeu* reported this to his mother, but she still could not believe that Prince Charming was male.

She persuaded her son to lay one more trap.

She told him to take his rescuer into the armory, and invite him to choose a weapon to take away with him as a present.

If he would choose one of the weapons decorated with precious stones, this would prove that Prince Charming was in fact a girl.

After lunch, the *zmeu* led Prince Charming to the armory.

There were, carefully arranged, all sorts of weapons.

Some were decorated with precious stones, others were undecorated.

The king's daughter, after examining all the weapons, chose for herself a rusty-looking sword, with the metal twisted into a coil.

Then she said to the *zmeu* and his mother that she wanted to leave the next day.

When the *zmeu*'s mother heard the kind of weapon Prince Charming had chosen, she was furious that she could not reveal the girl's disguise to her son.

"Even though Prince Charming seems to be

male based on his habits, he is in fact a girl, of the most cunning," she told her son.

However, seeing that she had no choice, she and her son went to the stables and gave Yellow Sun over to the king's daughter.

After they had all said their goodbyes, the king's daughter went on her way riding her horse, with Yellow Sun galloping alongside.

Once they were back on the road, the horse said to the girl:

"Mistress, up until now you have followed every piece of advice I have given you, and all has gone well for you. Follow my advice once more and you will not regret it. I am old and am getting increasingly scared of stumbling. Take my brother Yellow Sun and continue your journey with him. Trust him in the same way you have trusted me. He is much younger than I am and more agile, and will teach you the way I did, what to do when you need help."

"Your advice has indeed been excellent," the girl said. "But if I didn't know how loyal you were to my father, on this occasion I would not follow it. I will however trust your brother the way I have trusted you, once he proves that he has my best interests at heart."

"Trust me, mistress," said Yellow Sun. "I will be proud to have a brave woman such as yourself ride on my back. I will do my best so you do not feel my brother's absence. I want to protect him, as he is old, of the difficulties and dangers of the journey you intend to undertake. Because you should know that you will run into many difficulties and dangers. But with God's will and if you follow my advice, you will overcome them all and fulfill your mission."

The king's daughter mounted Yellow Sun and parted from her old horse, weeping.

They rode and rode, until the king's daughter saw a golden lock of hair lying by the side of the road.

She stopped Yellow Sun and asked him if she should take it or if she should leave it there.

"If you take it, you will regret it. But if you leave it, you will regret it as well. It is better if you take it," the horse said.

The girl took it, put it close to her chest, and they carried on.

They passed hills, mountains, and valleys, left forests rich and green in their wake, clearings with flowers the girl had never seen before, and streams with clear, cold water.

Eventually, they reached the court of the big and mighty king.

The other kings' sons who were serving at the mighty king's court came out to greet them.

The young men could not take their eyes away from the new arrival.

Both her words and her face charmed them.

The next day she went before the king and said why she had come.

The king couldn't contain his happiness that such a handsome and charming lad had arrived to serve him.

He was delighted with the lad's answers to his questions, as the young man was speaking with wisdom and humility.

The king became fond of his new servant and took him under his wing.

Time passed, and the king's daughter settled into her new life.

She found the other kings' sons stupid and impulsive, and did not want to associate with them.

They soon began hating her for keeping her distance and being favored by the king, and started plotting her downfall.

One day, the king's daughter cooked herself some food.

She was about to start eating when two sons of kings dropped by.

She invited them to eat with her.

The two kings' sons enjoyed the food so much that they licked their fingers when they finished eating.

They praised her for her cooking skills and said that they had never tasted anything as good.

During the meal, the two kings' sons also spotted the lock of hair the girl had found on the road.

They immediately recognized it as belonging to Ileana Samziana, a young maiden of legendary beauty.

As soon as these two kings' sons met the other kings' sons, they told them that they had eaten food cooked by the recent arrival, and it had tasted better than the food at the royal court.

Then all the kings' sons started pestering her to cook for the whole court.

One day, the opportunity arose to do so.

The royal cooks had gotten so drunk they weren't even able to light the fire in the stoves.

After being asked persistently, the king's daughter started cooking some excellent courses.

When her food was brought to the king, he could not stop delighting in it.

He called the head chef and told him to keep cooking like this from now on.

The head chef, knowing he would be unable to comply with the king's request and that it was better to own up to the truth, told the king who it was that had cooked that day.

Then the kings' sons told the king that the recently arrived king's son had in his possession a lock from Ileana Samziana's golden hair.

As soon as the king heard this, he ordered the new arrival to be brought before him at once.

"You have a lock of hair belonging to Ileana Samziana and haven't told me, even though I favored you over the others," the king said.

After the girl showed him the lock of hair, he said:

"I order you to bring me Ileana Samziana. If not, you will be put to death."

The poor king's daughter tried to protest, but the king had made up his mind.

She went to tell Yellow Sun what had just happened and ask for his advice.

"Do not fear, mistress," the horse said. "This very night my brother appeared to me in a dream to tell me that Ileana Samziana has been kidnapped by a *zmeu*. She told him that she won't love him until he presents her with her horde of mares, and the *zmeu* is at wit's end about how to fulfill her wish. In the meantime, he is keeping her in one of his castles among the sea marshes. Ask the king for a fleet of twenty ships, take the most beautiful wares as cargo, and we go find Ileana Samziana."

Upon hearing this, the king's daughter went straight to the king:

"Greetings, wise king. I have come to tell you that to complete the mission you have entrusted me with, I will need twenty ships and money to buy the most beautiful and expensive wares to take as cargo."

"Fine, but bring me Ileana Samziana," the king said.

As soon as the ships were ready, they loaded them with expensive gifts.

The king's daughter and Yellow Sun boarded the most beautiful of the ships and they set sail.

Neither the winds nor the waves of the sea could stand against them.

After several weeks, they reached the ocean marshes.

There they cast anchor.

Before going onto dry land, the king's daughter took from the ship a pair of slippers sewn with golden thread and decorated with precious stones.

She attached them to the front of her belt, as Yellow Sun had advised her to do.

As they wandered the shores, walking here and there, they spotted some palaces in the distance, which were rotating after the sun, and headed in their direction.

On the way they were confronted by three servants of the *zmeu,* who had been tasked with guarding Ileana Samziana.

But as soon as the servants laid their eyes on the slippers hanging from the king's daughter's belt, they relaxed their security measures.

They were eager to find out as much as they could about how the young lad sitting before them on his horse had come in possession of such exquisite items.

The young lad told them that he is a merchant and that he had gotten lost while sailing the seas.

He said he would be interested in speaking to their mistress to see if she would like to buy some of his wares.

Upon their return, the servants told Ileana Samziana what they had seen, and that the merchant was waiting outside the castle doors to speak to her.

Indeed, as she looked through her window, she could see the merchant.

As soon as she laid eyes on him, her heart started pounding.

So she told her servants that she wanted to meet the merchant and see these slippers for herself.

"If you were to do me the honor of accompanying me to my ships, I could show you wares that are even more beautiful and expensive than these puny slippers," the merchant said as Ileana Samziana was marveling at their beauty.

Ileana Samziana said she would indeed be keen to see these wares.

She entered one of the ships and was overwhelmed by the riches it carried.

While her eyes feasted upon the wares, the sailors pushed the ship away from dry land, and they were soon in the open sea.

When she eventually came to her senses and found herself in the middle of the ocean, Ileana Samziana pretended to be angry at having been misled.

She started arguing with the merchant that he had betrayed her trust.

But in her heart, she was praying to God to help them escape the terrible *zmeu* that had been keeping her captive.

They reached the shore safely.

But the *zmeu*'s mother, who had been informed by the servants that her soon-to-be daughter-in-law Ileana Samziana had been kidnapped by a sea merchant, had started chasing after them.

As soon as they set foot on shore, they saw her coming towards them like a lioness, with her maw open wide and casting enormous flames.

As soon as Ileana Samziana saw her, she realized who this terrible creature was.

She told the merchant, with whom she was riding on Yellow Sun, and started crying.

"What should I do?" the merchant asked Yellow Sun. "I don't know how much longer we can bear the heat coming from these flames."

"Put your hand in my left ear, take out the

wax that is there, and throw it behind you," Yellow Sun said.

The merchant did this.

A stone mountain erected itself behind them, so tall it could reach the sky.

For a few moments they thought they were safe.

But the *zmeu*'s mother managed to climb the mountain from crag to crag and kept on chasing them.

Ileana Samziana told the merchant that the *zmeu*'s mother was closing in.

After consulting with the horse, he pulled a hairbrush out of the horse's right ear and threw it behind them.

As soon as he did so, a rich forest sprang up in their wake, so thick that no beast could pass through it.

But the *zmeu*'s mother gnawed at the trees, swung herself from branch to branch, jumped from top to top, slithered through any small gaps in the undergrowth that she could find, and managed to make her way out of the forest.

Then she continued chasing after them, as fast and furious as a tornado.

When they saw that she had overcome this

obstacle as well, the merchant once again asked the horse what to do.

He said that Ileana Samziana should take off her engagement ring and throw it behind her.

As soon as she threw the ring, a wall erected itself behind them that reached up to the sky.

The *zmeu* 's mother, once she saw that she could neither climb over the wall nor gnaw at it, couldn't contain her rage.

Furious and filled with hatred, she climbed up and put her mouth next to the gap that the ring had left behind.

Through that tiny hole she blew fire from her cursed mouth for three hours, hoping that the fire would reach them and burn them to death.

But they took refuge at the bottom of the wall and were not harmed by the fire.

The *zmeu*'s mother blew and blew.

When she saw that she could neither kill nor catch them, the bile in her burst from anger.

She fell to the ground and died like a devil.

They waited a while until she had died for good, as Yellow Sun had taught them.

At that moment the wall disappeared as if it had never existed and the ring was back on Ileana Samziana's finger.

They continued their journey and kept going until they reached the royal court.

Upon arriving they went before the king, who received Ileana Samziana with great honor.

He could not contain his happiness and fell in love with her as soon as he saw her.

But Ileana Samziana was overcome with sadness.

"How is it possible," she thought, "that I seem to fall into the hands of men I cannot bear to even look at."

Her heart belonged to Prince Charming, who had saved her from the *zmeu*.

But the king said she had to marry him.

"Wise king, may you long reign over your kingdom," she said. "But I cannot marry you until you bring me my horde of mares along with the steed that guards them."

The king called in the king's daughter and said:

"Go and bring back Ileana Samziana's horde of mares and the steed that guards them. If not, you will be put to death."

"Powerful king," the king's daughter said, "I have only just returned from having accomplished the last difficult task you had entrusted me with, for which my life has been at stake. You have many brave kings' sons serving at your court. And because all find you a straightforward and God-fearing man, you would be within your right to give this task to someone else. I don't know anything about the horde of mares you are asking for."

"I don't care. Go find it, wherever it may be, and bring it here. And don't dare say another word."

The king's daughter bowed and went to tell Yellow Sun what she had been ordered to do.

"Go and find nine buffalo skins," the horse told her. "Dull them out and cover me with them. Do not fear, with God's help you will bring to good end this latest task the king has laden you with. And know that he will be made to suffer for his deeds in the end."

The king's daughter did as the horse had told her and they started on their journey.

On their way they came across the *zmeu* who was hoping to marry Ileana Samziana.

He was wandering like crazy, trying to figure out how to catch the horde of mares.

The king's daughter told him that Ileana Samziana has been kidnapped by a sea merchant and that his mother has died trying to rescue his beloved from the kidnapper.

Upon hearing this, the *zmeu* was furious.

His eyes became blurry with anger and he could no longer see.

Then, when he realized that he was in fact speaking with the kidnapper of his beloved, he lost his temper from anger and grief.

And roaring like a lion, he battled with the king's daughter, who was keeping her cool and whom the horse was encouraging and helping.

When Yellow Sun would see that the *zmeu* was preparing to strike, he would rise higher than the *zmeu*.

The *zmeu*'s blows would be thrown at the air, thus wasting energy for no gain.

When, on the other hand, the king's daughter was about to strike, the horse would drop quickly towards the *zmeu*'s horse and she would strike into his bare flesh.

They fought so hard the earth shook beneath them.

Eventually, the king's daughter was able to bring her sword crossways and cut off the *zmeu*'s head.

Then, leaving his carcass to the crows and

the magpies to feast on, she and Yellow Sun continued their journey.

Eventually, they reached the place where the horde of mares was.

The mares were grazing peacefully by themselves, without any steed in sight.

The horse told the king's daughter to climb up a tree.

As soon as she did, he neighed three times and the entire horde of mares gathered around him.

Then the steed appeared, foaming at the mouth and snorting from fury.

When he saw Yellow Sun amongst his mares, he charged against him with fury.

A fight broke out between them.

From her hiding place up in the tree, the king's daughter could see what was happening.

She saw that when the steed was attacking Yellow Sun, he was biting chunks from the buffalo skins, leaving Yellow Sun unharmed.

On the other hand, when Yellow Sun was attacking the steed, he was biting from bare flesh.

They fought until the steed, wounded from head to tail and full of blood, was conquered.

Yellow Sun escaped unharmed, covered by the buffalo skins which had been torn to shreds.

The king's daughter climbed down from the tree and mounted Yellow Sun.

They took charge of the horde of mares, guiding them from the back, while the steed barely dragged himself behind them.

After they brought the horde of mares and the steed into the king's yard, the king's daughter went to let him know they had accomplished their task.

In the meantime, Ileana Samziana came out into the yard and called her beloved animals by their name.

The steed, as soon as he heard her call his name, shook himself three times and made himself whole again, without a single wound left on him.

Ileana Samziana said to the king to ask someone to milk the mares, so they can have a bath in their milk.

But who could get anywhere near them?

At the slightest attempt, the mares were kicking so hard with their hooves that anything they hit would fly off.

As nobody could approach them, the king

once again ordered the king's daughter to take on the task.

The king's daughter was outraged that it was always she who was asked to undertake the most difficult tasks.

But as she had a clear conscience, she prayed to God to help her bring this task to a good end.

As soon as she finished her prayer, a heavy rain started, pouring in buckets.

Soon the water reached the knees of the mares.

The rain was followed by a severe frost, which kept the mares glued to their spot.

Seeing this miracle, the king's daughter thanked God for His help and started milking the mares.

The king could no longer contain his love for Ileana Samziana.

He was looking at her like to a ripe cherry tree.

She however did not even deign to look at him, but kept postponing the wedding day after day.

"I see, wise king, that I have received all I have asked for," she told him. "I only need one more thing, and then we can marry."

"My dove," the king answered, "my kingdom and myself are your obedient servants. Ask for anything you want and I will make sure you get it, because I cannot contain my love for you. I have become dizzy, I dream while awake, I no longer know what I am doing when I look into your beautiful eyes."

"Bring me the baptism urn which is kept in a little church over the Jordan waters," Ileana Samziana said, "and then we can marry."

The king called the king's daughter to him and ordered her to do whatever it takes to bring back what Ileana Samziana had asked for.

The king's daughter went to tell Yellow Sun of this latest order and to ask what she should do.

"This is the last and most difficult task you have to accomplish," he said. "But put your trust in God, because the king's days are numbered."

They got ready and left.

On the way, Yellow Sun told the king's daughter:

"The baptism urn is located on a table in the middle of a small church and is guarded by a group of nuns. They do not sleep, day and night. From time to time however, a hermit visits them and tells them of the holy things. When they are assembled to listen to what the hermit is teaching them, only one remains on guard. If we could arrive at that time, things will work out well. If not, who knows how long we'll have to wait, because that is the only way."

They went, therefore, over the Jordan waters and reached the small church.

Luckily the hermit had just arrived and assembled the nuns to listen to him.

Only one had remained on guard.

And this one, being tired due to the long wait, had started drifting off to sleep.

She took precautionary measures, however, and laid herself to sleep on the threshold.

She thought that by doing so, nobody could get in without waking her up.

Yellow Sun taught the king's daughter what to do to get hold of the baptism urn.

The girl sneaked along the wall and gently, walking on the tips of her toes, she reached the door.

As nimble as a cat, she jumped over the threshold, not even touching the nun who had fallen asleep.

Grabbing hold of the urn, she came out as she had entered, got on the horse, and set off.

The nun heard Yellow Sun galloping in the distance and jumped up.

Seeing that the urn was missing, she started screaming and wailing so bitterly, it would melt anyone's heart.

The other nuns immediately gathered around her and started wailing about the theft of their beloved urn.

The hermit, seeing that the urn was beyond reach, looked towards the king's daughter as she was flying away on Yellow Sun.

With his hands up to the sky and kneeling, he cursed her.

"Holy Lord!" he said. "Make it so that the unlawful one who has dared put their unholy hands on the baptism urn becomes a woman, if they are a man. And if they are a woman, make them become a man!"

The hermit's prayer was immediately heeded.

The king's daughter became a young man so handsome you would fall in love looking at him.

As the young lad reached the king's court, he felt that he was no longer the way he was when he had left.

Now he was handsomer and fiercer.

"Powerful king," he said, as he handed over the urn, "I have undertaken the things you have tasked me with. I hope that now I have finished. Be happy and reign in peace for as long as Lord's mercy will be with you."

"I am satisfied with the way you have completed your tasks," said the king. "After my death, it is you who will take the reins of the kingdom, because until now I have had no heir. And if God will give me a son, you will be his right hand."

Ileana Samziana, seeing that her latest request had been granted, decided to take her revenge on the king for always sending out her beloved to complete all the dangerous tasks.

She ordered to heat up the bath so that she and the king could bathe in the milk of her mares.

After she got into the bath, she ordered to bring in the steed to blow cold air.

The steed blew from one nostril cool air towards her, and with the other nostril fiery air towards the king.

Even the king's insides got boiled, and he died on the spot.

There was a big uproar throughout the

kingdom when people heard of the death of the mighty and powerful king.

People from all parts gathered and organized a funeral fit for an almighty king.

After this, Ileana Samziana said to Prince Charming:

"It is you who brought me here, you who brought my horde of mares and the steed guarding them, you who killed the *zmeu* who had kidnapped me, you who brought me the baptism urn. It is you whom I choose as my husband. Let's have a bath and get married."

They agreed and got into the bath.

Ileana called her steed to warm up the milk in which they would bathe.

The new king also called in Yellow Sun.

And the two horses competed over which would make the most comfortable bath for their master.

After bathing together, they got married the next day and ascended to the throne of the kingdom.

The feast lasted three weeks long.

Everyone was happy that God had given them such a brave king, who had already accomplished so many great deeds.

And he reigned with righteousness and fear of God, protecting the poor and not oppressing anyone.

The king and queen may still be reigning to this day if they haven't yet died.

I happened to be around, gawking at the wedding feast.

Then I got onto my horse and told you the story thus.

TRANSLATOR'S NOTE (THE GIRL WHO WOULD BE KING)

As I mentioned in the introduction, this was the story that started this entire translation project for me.

I was amazed and delighted to find a full-blown transgender story in a Romanian book of fairy tales, let alone one dating from the 19th century.

This tale's original title is *Ileana Samziana*, which is strange, as she is not the main protagonist.

In translating and adapting this story, I wanted the title to reflect that this is a transgender story.

Of course, this is not a transgender story in the contemporary sense of the word.

The protagonist does not experience body dysphoria, nor do they show any sense of struggling with their identity or the way they are perceived by others.

At the end, they seem to simply embrace the transformation and go along with it.

However, I find the existence of a 19th century story in which the character starts out as female and ends up as male simply extraordinary.

Before being collected and published by Petre Ispirescu, this story must have traveled from person to person, being told and retold many times over a long period of time.

How extraordinary that this story has resonated with enough people that it has survived long enough to be written down formally.

Even more extraordinary is the fact that it was published as part of the most celebrated collection of fairy tales in the Romanian language.

Of course, it is ironic that a story that seems so far ahead of its time would display so many patriarchal values.

As a woman living in the 21st century, I

found some of the judgements about the differences between men and women somewhat difficult to digest.

I made the choice to keep these elements, as they were integral to the story.

However, I did take out one particularly offensive line towards the end.

In that line, the new king says to Ileana Samziana something along the lines of 'but do not forget who wears the trousers in this relationship'.

That line simply had to go.

As you have been reading this story, you may have wondered about the use of the title Prince Charming, which appears several times in my translation.

The original is *Fat Frumos*, which is a name often given to the male hero in Romanian fairy tales.

A literal translation might be 'Handsome Youth' or 'Lad Handsome' (*frumos* means 'handsome' and *fat* refers to a young man).

I chose Prince Charming as this name fits the hero's role in the story and is well-known to English-speaking readers.

While reading, you may have also wondered what a *zmeu* is.

The *zmeu* (plural *zmei*) is a monster-like creature that appears in many Romanian fairy tales, legends, and myths.

Because the *zmeu* appears so often in these stories, this creature is never described, presumably because the people listening to these tales had a common understanding of what a *zmeu* looks like.

However, it is worth pointing out that there is no formal consensus over what a *zmeu* looks like.

This lack of clear description is perhaps why the *zmeu* is so popular in Romanian fairy tales.

Its monster-like features can easily be adapted by the storyteller to take the shape of whatever is needed by the narrative.

Some depictions show the *zmeu* as more human-like, while in others the *zmeu* seems to share a stronger resemblance to dragons.

If you are curious, I suggest you type the word into Google Images and enjoy the many different representations you will find.

I decided to add a short yet somewhat vague description of the *zmeu* ('fearsome human-like creatures with magic powers') in my translated version.

My intention was to indicate to the reader that the word refers to a fantastic creature that is part of Romanian folklore, while at the same time not limiting the reader's imagination to my own mental image of a *zmeu*.

The *zmeu* shares many human features.

Based on what happens in the stories, we can tell that the *zmeu* has arms and legs, as well as the ability to ride a horse and use weapons.

On the other hand, the *zmeu* is often described as having a tail and being able to blow fire through their mouth, as well as being bigger and stronger than humans.

In some stories, the *zmeu* also has other magical powers, such as being able to shapeshift, often as part of their plan to trap and defeat the hero.

In most cases, the *zmeu* is an evil, cunning creature that attempts to kidnap a beautiful maiden and force her into becoming his wife, as is the case with Ileana Samziana in the tale you have just read.

The *zmeu* is often helped by his mother, who usually has a whole range of magic powers and chases after the hero or attempts to outwit him once her son has been defeated.

Although, as you can see in this story, the *zmeu* is not always destructive.

In this story, for instance, you encounter two mother-son *zmeu* pairings where you can observe different kinds of behavior.

The first *zmeu* and his mother are courteous towards the king's daughter and largely helpful.

Even though they could kidnap her, or not fulfill their promise of handing Yellow Sun to her, they do none of these things.

However, this kind of behavior is not common among the *zmei* you will encounter in most Romanian fairy tales.

The actions of the second mother-son *zmeu* pair are more common of the way the zmeu is often portrayed in Romanian fairy tales.

The interactions with this second pair also show many beloved tropes: kidnapping a beautiful maiden who has to be rescued by the hero, the chase and the many obstacles the hero has to put up in order to escape, and the attempt by the mother of the *zmeu* to kill through blowing fire on the hero, which seems to be the undoing of many of the *zmeu* mothers as this attempt generally fails.

If you decide to read more of my translated stories of Petre Ispirescu's collection, you will no doubt see some of these tropes in action in a variety of different stories.

THE MAGIC BULL

There was once an old man and an old woman.

The old man had a son from his first wife and the old woman a daughter from her first husband.

The old woman couldn't stand the old man's son.

"Husband!" she said one day. "If you don't send your son away from here, I will no longer be your wife."

"Where would I send him?" said the old man. "Let him grow up some more and then we'll send him to his own home."

"No. I want him out of the house now. You must choose between him and me."

The old man, seeing there's no way around this with his wife, said to the boy:

"My son, I'm old, as you can see. I am not as strong as I used to be. Your stepmother wants you to leave. Go wherever God will lead you, to earn your living."

"I can see that my stepmother can't stand me," the boy said. "I don't know why. I haven't disobeyed her. I do everything she asks, but in vain. I will go wherever God will lead me, and I will find a way to earn my living. I have youth on my side. When you'll be able to, dad, come and see me, because otherwise I will shrivel up from missing you."

"Stay in good health, my son, and may God help you."

"Stay well, dad."

And the poor boy left home with tears running down his cheeks.

He went out into the world to look for work and eventually came across a wealthy man who hired him as his servant.

The boy worked as a servant for seven years, and his master was happy with him.

But eventually, the boy started missing his father so much, he couldn't bear it any longer.

So he told his master he would like to go home.

"Lad, you have served me for seven years," his master said. "I like how you served me. Does my bread no longer taste good to you? Or is anyone offering you more elsewhere? Is that why you want to leave my service?"

"No, master. But I am homesick, and I would like to see my father again. If you feel I am due anything after my service, please let me have it before I go."

"Fine, lad, you can't keep a servant against their will. When you started working for me, we didn't strike up an agreement about how much I owed you when you left. But as payment for the work you have done for me, I will let you choose from my herd two large animals and ten small ones."

When the boy heard that he is given so much, he thought his master was joking.

"Master, you said you liked the way I served you," he said. "Why are you making fun of me?"

"Are you not happy with the payment I am giving you?"

"Of course I am, master. But you know I haven't bargained with you, so you can give me whatever you like. If what you say is true, then I feel it is too much, unless you are jesting with me."

"I didn't mean to jest, lad, there's no reason to. You have behaved honorably and have served me loyally. The animals I have told you to choose are fitting for your service."

The lad couldn't contain his joy, especially when he realized that it was through his labor that he had earned so many animals.

He went to the smaller animals, looked at each of them in turn, and wondered which ones to choose.

He didn't want to choose from among the best animals, because he didn't think his work was worth as much.

He also didn't want to choose the worst ones, because his heart wouldn't let him.

He therefore chose from among the animals in the middle.

He was going to do the same with the large animals.

But when it came to choosing those, his attention fell upon a bull which was looking at the boy with a mischievous twinkle in his eye.

The boy chose this bull and a cow.

Then he set off on his way home, hoping that

bringing this much wealth with him will appease his stepmother's resentment towards him.

When the boy reached home, his father was overwhelmed with joy.

His son had grown into a handsome young lad.

But his stepmother hated him just as much as before.

The son helped his father with all the work in the field and with taking the animals out to pasture.

He did everything he could to make himself useful to the household, but his stepmother kept thinking up new ways to make his life a misery.

In the mornings, when he would take the animals to pasture, his stepmother would give him a cake to eat as his lunch.

But she would bake it out of the ashes from the fireplace and he couldn't eat it.

At lunchtime, instead of eating like everyone else, he would sit underneath the shadow of a tree, feeling sorry for himself.

He didn't want to tell his father so as not to cause any trouble.

Nor was he getting any peace at home.

This was making him sad, deep in thought, and without joy.

One day, while crying from hunger at lunch time, the bull, whom the boy had named 'Talerus', started speaking to him.

"Master, don't be sad," Talerus said. "Forget that cake made of ashes. Take my right horn and eat and drink whatever you want out of it."

The lad was stunned to hear his bull speaking to him.

"Listen to my advice," Talerus said. "You are a good lad and I feel pity for you. You are wasting your youth, crying about things that cannot be changed. Do as I say and you will see that it works."

The boy took the right horn from Talerus.

Inside it, he was astounded to find a loaf of bread as white as snow and a glass of wine that would make you lick your lips.

He ate and drank to his heart's content.

His stepmother noticed after a while that the lad's face had become fuller and that he was doing everything with great joy.

Instead of watching him waste away, as she had hoped, he was thriving.

She suspected that Talerus must be the cause of the boy's new-found happiness.

The boy was fussing over him and spending more time with him than with the other animals.

She asked her daughter to follow the boy and to watch what he does when taking the animals to pasture.

Her daughter followed him, saw everything, returned to her mother and said:

"Mother, what I saw today is beyond belief. My stepbrother's bull has magic powers."

"Didn't I tell you there must be something odd about that bull?"

"You should have seen, mother, how my step-brother would take the bull by the neck and kiss him on one side and another, making my heart go all fluttery. Then at noon, he took his right horn and got out of it some bread, white and well baked, and some wine. And he ate them with such joy, I felt hungry watching him. But what really shocked me was that I heard the bull talking."

"I must find a way to get rid of that bull," the mother said.

The following day, she told her husband he

has to slaughter the bull and started nagging him relentlessly about it.

The poor old man tried in vain to stand his ground.

He told her the bull wasn't theirs to slaughter, it belonged to his son.

When this didn't work, he told her that the bull was beautiful and would come in useful one day.

But his wife kept nagging him and wouldn't let go until she made him agree to slaughter the bull.

The boy, fortunately, was clever and heard it all.

As soon as daylight came, he went to Talerus and told him what was about to happen.

The bull told him to wait on the porch.

When they will chase him to bring him to slaughter, Talerus will pass by the porch.

The boy will jump on his back, and they will run away together.

This is what they did.

After escaping death, Talerus took his master to a forest more beautiful than the lad had ever seen.

Close-by were some orchards with grass to graze on, always green and in bloom.

There they made a hut and lived a life of plenty.

One day, the boy was sitting in front of the hut playing his flute, while Talerus was grazing in the nearby orchard.

An enormous bull came by, so fat he seemed to be bursting out of his skin.

"Why did you come here, lad, with your bull, to drink my water and eat my grass?" he asked.

"I didn't know this was your land," the lad said. "My bull brought me here."

"Tell him to come tomorrow morning to the golden attic, to fight me."

After that, he left.

In the evening, Talerus found the boy sadder than ever.

"What is it, master, why are you so sad?" Talerus asked.

The boy told Talerus everything the fat bull had said.

"Leave it to me, master, don't worry about it."

The next morning, Talerus left the boy at the hut.

He went to the golden attic and fought the other bull.

Talerus emerged victorious and placed the other bull's corpse underneath the attic.

Then he returned home safe and unharmed.

Two days later, another bull came by, not as big as the first.

He told the boy the same as the previous one, and asked that Talerus fights him at the silver attic.

As the first time, Talerus found the boy sad and crying.

He calmed him down as before and went to fight the other bull.

After emerging victorious, he put the other bull's corpse underneath the attic as well.

Several days later another bull came.

This one was thin, ugly, and full of scabs.

He told the boy:

"Who has given you permission to come here with your bull, drink my water, and graze on my grass?"

"What's it to you?" the boy said.

"If it wasn't of any concern to me, who else should it be?" said the bull. "Which of you two will dare fight with me, should come tomorrow to the copper attic."

"Go in peace," the boy said, "we'll come."

When Talerus returned from grazing in the evening, the boy joyfully told him everything that had happened.

"Your joy isn't good, master," the bull said, "now my turn has come. That bull, scabby and skinny, will conquer me. You should be present at our fight. I won't let you fight with him. You are young, naïve, and you have much to see in this world. Once he has vanquished me and has put me underneath the attic, jump in and take my left horn. Don't open it until you get back home."

When the boy heard this, he couldn't stop crying.

His heart hurt so much he couldn't sleep all night.

Early next morning, Talerus went to the copper attic.

There he waited for the downtrodden bull.

When the bull arrived, they started to fight.

And they fought, and fought, until towards noon.

At times Talerus was bringing the other bull

down, at other times the downtrodden bull was bringing Talerus down.

Then they fought with their horns and neither of them could conquer the other.

By the afternoon, Talerus had lost much of his power.

The other bull charged against him and put him underneath the attic.

The boy jumped in and took his left horn.

He lingered by the attic, crying and crying.

But when, towards dusk, Talerus still hadn't come back from underneath the attic, the boy left carrying the horn, crushed by grief.

He spent the night on a little hill.

The next day, he was famished.

He thought he might find some food inside the horn he had taken from Talerus, and opened it.

Suddenly, a multitude of cattle and flocks and all sorts of animals came out.

How could he get them all home?

He didn't know how to put them back in the horn, and he would have needed an army of servants to herd them homewards.

He started to cry bitterly.

While he was crying, a dragon came by and said:

"What will you give me, boy, to put all these animals back inside the horn?'

"I will give you half of them," the boy said.

"That's not what I want," the dragon said. "I want something else."

"Tell me what you want."

"I want you to promise that when you least expect it, I can take the one thing you love most and devour it."

The boy, without realizing what he was doing, agreed to the bargain.

The dragon cracked his tail three times and put all the cattle back inside the horn.

Then the boy took the horn and returned to his father.

He found his father on his own, because the old woman and her daughter had abandoned him.

When the old man saw his son having become a man, he was overcome with happiness.

His son opened the horn and suddenly the entire field and all the neighboring fields filled up with animals.

"All these are yours?" the old man asked.

"Yes, dad. What should we do with so many animals?"

"Soothe the troubles of the widows and the poor," the old man said.

The boy listened to his father's advice.

Every day from then on, he did good to those who needed help.

Eventually, there wasn't a single poor person left in their village.

News traveled to the royal court about the riches and mercy of the old man's son.

The king had a wise and beautiful young daughter, and he decided that the old man's son would make an excellent son in law.

He therefore sent messengers to the boy, to offer him his daughter's hand in marriage.

The boy was surprised to hear about the king's offer.

He went to the royal court and behaved with much grace and wisdom.

The king was delighted with his choice, and his daughter fell in love with the boy, because he was handsome and clever.

They soon came to an agreement, and the young couple got married.

The boy's father, who had been invited to the

wedding, waited until after the dancing and rejoicing had died down and everyone was on their way home.

Then, following an old custom, he went to the couple's bedroom and put a loaf of white bread on the table.

Then he too returned home.

During the night, the dragon appeared before the boy and told him he is coming to get his end of the bargain.

He asked him to hand over his bride, whom the boy loved with all his heart, so the dragon could devour her.

The old man's son, who had forgotten about this agreement, didn't know what to do.

He didn't want to fight with the dragon to kill him, because he knew this had been their agreement.

His father had taught him that how one's word of honor turns out, so does the soul.

But nor could he bear letting his beloved get devoured by the dragon.

He was overcome by inner turmoil about what to do, so he doesn't break his word yet doesn't let his bride die a horrible death.

Suddenly, the loaf of bread on the table

started to jump and say:

"He has sown me, I have grown. He has cut me with the sickle, has tied me in bundles and I have put up with it. You put up with it too, and disappear into the depths of the ocean."

The dragon kept still and listened.

The bread spoke again:

"Afterwards the horses stepped on me, and he took me to the mill. Put up with it like I have, and go away so we don't hear from you again."

The dragon kept listening, but the tongues in his mouth were playing like lightning.

The bride and groom kept quiet.

The bread spoke again:

"Then he ground me, and after bringing me home, he put me through a sieve, mixed me with water, put me in the oven, baked me to make my eyes pop, and I put up with it. Put up with it too, blasted dragon, may you burst!"

The noise the dragon made when he burst was so great that everyone in the royal palace heard it and woke up.

When they rushed to the matrimonial suite, what did they find?

An enormous dragon, burst and sliced.

He was so large everyone got a fright.

They took the corpse outside the palace and gave it to the crows to eat.

Then the groom told everyone the entire story.

When the people in the palace heard, they thanked God that a miracle had happened to save the bride and groom from harm.

The young couple lived in peace, doing good everywhere.

They might still be alive today if they haven't yet died.

And I got into a saddle and told you the story thus.

TRANSLATOR'S NOTE (THE MAGIC BULL)

The original title of this story is *Talerus*, which is the name of the magic bull.

If you are a non-Romanian speaker and want to have a go at pronouncing this name, the 's' at the end is pronounced 'sh'.

You may have raised an eyebrow at the part of the story where the king offers the boy his daughter's hand in marriage.

At that point in the story, there is no mention of the girl's interest in her potential future husband.

As a translator, I chose not to add anything to this part of the story about the girl's potential interest, as I feel it is important that I stay true to the original as much as possible.

However, I feel it is important to draw your attention to this part of the story, in case you choose to tell this story yourself.

If you wanted, it would be easy to add something at this point that gives the girl more agency and choice.

Maybe the daughter could have heard of the boy's reputation, and become interested in meeting him?

Perhaps the father was acting in accordance to his daughter's wishes?

For any storytellers out there wanting to use this tale, these kinds of additions may make this story more relevant to a contemporary audience.

The dragon in this story is a *balaur*, which is the Romanian version of this type of creature.

I chose not to use the Romanian term, as depictions of the *balaur* show a creature that any Western readers would easily recognize as a dragon.

However, it is worth noting that in some Romanian stories, the term *balaur* can occasionally refer to any monster-like creature, not just dragons.

THE FAIRY QUEEN

Once upon a time, there was a powerful king who had three sons.

As the sons were nearing marrying age, the king started to wonder how to help them find their soulmate so they could have happy marriages.

One night, the king had a dream that provided him with an answer.

The next day, he called his sons and they went to the top of a high tower.

He asked each of his sons to strike an arrow.

"Where your arrows falls," the king said, "that is where you will find your soulmate."

The sons obeyed their father, because they trusted him.

They struck their arrow, and that of the eldest son fell on the roof of the palace belonging to a neighboring king.

The middle son's arrow fell on the roof of the house belonging to one of the highest ranking aristocrats.

But the arrow of the youngest son flew into the heights of the sky.

They all craned their necks looking for it, and almost lost is from sight.

Then they saw it falling down and landing into a tall tree in the middle of a large forest.

The eldest son went to the neighboring king's court, where he got engaged with the king's daughter, and brought her back to his father.

The middle son went to the house of the high ranking aristocrat, where he got engaged to the aristocrat's daughter, and also brought her back to his father.

The youngest set off as well, but he did not know where to go.

He scoured the earth until he eventually found the large forest where his arrow had landed.

He made his way through the undergrowth

until he found the tree into which his arrow had struck.

This tree was tall, thick, and old.

The boy climbed it until he reached a spot where he could hang from one of its branches.

And from branch to branch, at times hanging from his hands, at times from his feet crossed and held tightly together, he reached the top of the tree.

There he grabbed the arrow and pulled it out.

He climbed down with his soul full of bitterness and sadness.

He worried that he would never find his soulmate, because what is there to find in that tree?

As if it hadn't been enough that he hadn't found the one destined for him, and that he had made this whole trip in vain, he realized, as he was about to leave the tree, that an owl was hanging from his back.

He tried wiggling his back in all directions, but the owl had stuck her claws into his back and would not let go.

He twisted and turned, to escape the plague, but there was no way.

Seeing that nothing worked, he decided to

return home with the owl on his back and figure out later how to get rid of it.

On the way he noticed that six other owls were also following him.

He went, the poor lad, with the flock of owls following him.

He arranged to arrive home at night, so he wouldn't be laughed at by anyone he would encounter.

As soon as he entered his bedroom, the six owls perched themselves wherever they found a spot.

And the seventh owl, which had fastened itself to his back, unfastened herself and jumped into his bed.

As he was exhausted from the long journey and all the mishaps along the way, he fell asleep as soon as his head hit the pillow, as if someone had knocked him out.

The next day, he couldn't believe his eyes when he found next to him in bed a fairy so beautiful that whoever would look at her would remain speechless.

And at the end of the bed were six female servants, one more beautiful than the other.

He also saw, in the corner of the room, seven owl skins, thrown one on top of the other.

When his parents met the fairy and her servants, they were overwhelmed by their beauty.

Not long passed, and the day of the eldest brother's wedding arrived.

The youngest son went to the celebrations with his fiancée.

There was no one like her in the entire kingdom and he was proud to show her off.

All the wedding guests were overwhelmed by her beauty.

As she was already taken, the other kings' sons who had been invited to the wedding were flirting with her servants, competing with one another for the opportunity to dance with them.

In the evening, they went to dinner and feasted late into the night.

The king's youngest son slept well that night, but when he got up in the morning and saw the owl skins lying next to the bed, he felt disgusted.

Soon the middle son's wedding day arrived.

The youngest son was once again accompanied by the fairy.

His heart was full of joy and pride, especially

as he could see all the other kings' sons were following her every move and pining after her.

To distract themselves, they were dancing with the fairy's servants.

In the evening, they went to dinner.

The youngest son, tempted by the devil, got up from the table, went to his room, and cast the owl skins into the fire.

Then he returned to the table without telling his fiancée what he had done.

"Mistress, we are in danger!" one of the servants screamed as soon as he returned.

"Mistress, I can smell burning!" another one said. "Bad things are about to happen to us."

"Be quiet," the fairy said, "you are probably imagining things and disturbing this wonderful dinner."

But a third servant said:

"Mistress, there is no escape, we have been betrayed."

Meanwhile, the fairy too had started sensing that something was wrong.

Suddenly, they all got up from the table and transformed into doves.

Then the fairy said to the youngest son:

"You have betrayed my trust. I will now

leave, and you will never see me again, unless you find my dwelling place, which no other human has so far managed to do."

They flew up into the sky and disappeared from view.

In vain did the wedding guests ask the youngest son to return to the table.

Nor did his parents and brothers succeed in making him forget his grief.

His eyes kept searching for the doves.

The next day before dawn he got ready to look for his fiancée.

Without her, life had lost its meaning.

He said goodbye to his family and went on his quest.

He passed hills, valleys, and dark forests through which nobody had walked before.

He made his way through marshes and ponds, yet could not find the flock of doves.

The lad was wrestling with himself, searching, looking, questioning, but he was not making any progress.

With his heart broken, his soul crushed from grief, and burning from lost love, he was pushing himself beyond the point of exhaustion, but all in vain.

At times the thought crossed his mind that he could simply end his life, throw himself into an abyss or smash his skull against some mountain crags.

But his heart seemed to tell him that one day, all these troubles would come to an end.

In those moments, he would come back to himself and continue his journey with even more zeal.

The hope that was keeping him going was that whoever searches in detail and persistently is bound to find a way to accomplish the task they have set themselves.

One day, broken from exhaustion, he went into a clearing, to rest for a little while.

And while sitting there, he drifted off to sleep.

He suddenly heard voices and woke up.

To his amazement, he saw three devils arguing with one another.

They were so passionate about their argument they were foaming at the mouth.

He went to them and said:

"Argument without a fight is like a wedding without the band."

"Your words make no sense," they responded.

"But we were not arguing, we were only disagreeing."

"And what were you disagreeing over?" he asked. "Because the racket you are making is loud enough to wake up the dead."

"It's about the fact that we have inherited, from our father, a pair of galoshes, a hat, and a whip, and we cannot agree who should take what."

"And what are they good for, these items you are disagreeing over?"

"When someone puts on the galoshes, they are able to walk over the sea as if it was dry land. When they put on the hat, not even the devil can see them, even when poking him in the eye with his finger. And if someone takes the whip in their hand and hits their enemies with it, whoever gets hit will transform into stone."

"You are right to disagree. Because without the other items, each of your inheritances aren't worth two frozen onions. If you are prepared to listen to what I am about to suggest, I may be able to give you justice."

"We are listening," the devils said in one voice, "tell us what to do."

"Can you see those three mountains ahead of

you? Each of you should climb up one of them. Whoever will be the first to return, after I have given you a signal, can take ownership of all three items."

"What a great suggestion! That's what we'll do. Well done! Looks like we have found the person to do us justice."

And they immediately set off towards the mountains, each going towards a different one.

In the meantime, our lad put the galoshes on his feet, the hat on his head, and took the whip in his hand.

When the devils reached the top of the mountains and waited for the signal, the king's youngest son cracked his whip once in front of each mountain and turned the devils into stone.

Then he went on his way, letting his heart guide him.

He had barely taken ten steps when he saw above him a flock of seven doves.

He followed them with his eyes until he saw where they landed and set off in that direction.

His galoshes made it possible to walk over oceans, rivers, and large expanses of water as if walking on dry land.

Then he made his way through cities and

deserts, until he reached a mountain so tall it seemed to touch the sky.

That is where the doves had landed.

He started climbing the mountain and, from cave to cave, from crag to crag, from precipice to precipice, climbing at times along the edges, at times along the slopes, he reached a cave.

He went into the cave, and was thunderstruck when he found a palace built with such craft you cannot find on this earth.

There lived his fiancée, the Fairy Queen.

As soon as he saw her walking through the gardens with the servants following her, he recognized her.

A cute little boy was following her too, running, playing among the flowers, and asking the fairy to show him this or that butterfly.

It looks like the fairy had been pregnant when she had flown from the dinner table, and this was their son.

The king's son could barely contain his happiness.

He wanted to run like a madman, to take his son in his arms and kiss him.

But he refrained from doing so, because he did not want to scare him.

Nobody had seen him yet, as he was made invisible by using his hat.

Evening had started to fall, and he still hadn't decided how to show himself.

Eventually he heard the servants inviting the fairy to the table for dinner.

He went as well and sat himself in-between the fairy and his son.

The servants brought in the food.

He was famished, as it had been a long time since he had eaten properly, so he started eating.

The fairy wondered how it was that the food was getting eaten so quickly.

She ordered more food, but even this food got eaten within instants.

While eating he would at times lift his hat a little towards the child.

"Look at daddy, mummy!" the boy said the first time he saw his father.

"Your father, my dear, won't come to us until he learns some powerful magic," his mother said.

The king's son quickly pulled the hat back over his eyes and got back to eating.

He was eating so much you'd think a pack of wolves were fighting over the food.

After he finished this food too, the fairy, baffled by this, asked for more.

The king's son once again showed himself to the boy, overjoyed that his son had recognized him.

The child once again told his mother.

She told him off, because she could not believe that her fiancé was ever going to learn to perform the magic that would allow him to find her.

She knew that no living being from the other world could reach the place where they lived, unless they were able to use powerful magic.

The child was silent, because his father had pulled the hat back over his eyes again.

The king's son continued eating until this food too was all gone.

He kept eating, yet was still hungry for more.

As there was no food left to bring to the table, the fairy started worrying that there is nothing left for her servants.

When, once again, the little boy cried out:

"Mum, I swear, it's dad."

"So where is he, then? What are you on about?"

"I'm not on about anything. Look, there next to me, he is taking me into his arms."

The fairy got a fright when she heard this.

But the little boy wouldn't stop until his father decided to show himself, to reassure his fiancée.

"Here I am," he said, taking off his hat. "You did not believe our son when he told you he saw me. I did not know what to believe when I saw those disgusting skins. I thought I was doing well setting them on fire, to help you get rid of them."

"It's how we've been destined to suffer," the fairy said. "Leave all these past things be, and tell me how you have managed to reach this place."

And after they told each other about all that had happened, and all their mishaps, they embraced, kissed their son, and stayed together.

After a while, the king's son persuaded the fairy to return to the world of humans.

They went to the king, the lad's father, and there they had a wedding so big that it became famous throughout the entire world.

As the king was getting older, his people asked that his youngest son follow him to the throne, because he had a good mind and was fair in his judgement.

And they lived and ruled in great happiness, so much so their name was preserved for all eternity.

And I got into a saddle and told you the story thus.

TRANSLATOR'S NOTE (THE FAIRY QUEEN)

The original title is *Zana Zanelor*, which in a literal translation would be 'The Fairy of Fairies'.

In my translation, I said that the middle brother's arrow falls on the house of one of the highest ranking aristocrats.

In the original, the actual term used is *boiar*.

This points to a person of high status in the Romanian feudal system, but it does not have an exact translation in the English language.

I chose to use 'aristocrat' because this is the closest Western equivalent.

However, I thought I should mention the word *boiar* here, in case you would like to look up this interesting role within the Romanian feudal system.

Another translation choice I made is that in the original version, the six women serving the Fairy Queen are described as her slaves.

However, using the word 'slave' makes me feel deeply uncomfortable, and I would guess many readers would feel the same way.

I therefore chose to use the word 'servant' instead.

This word does not detract from the story itself, yet is more relatable from our modern-day perspective.

Overall, I was delighted to find this tale, as it provides an alternative to a well-known and much-loved story trope.

We are familiar with a woman having to go through many trials to correct a mistake she has made and win back the love of her life.

The female version of this quest appears in stories that are well-known in the West, such as *East of the Sun and West of the Moon*, and the story of *Eros and Psyche.*

In Petre Ispirescu's collection, you will find this trope in *Princess Pig*, which is the headline story in *Princess Pig and Other Romanian Fairy Tales*.

But in this story, it is the male character who has to go on a quest.

This is a refreshing alternative to the better-known story trope depicting the female quest.

DEATH'S CALL

There was once a man who would pray to God every day to make him rich.

His frequent prayers found God in a good mood one day, and God listened.

As the man got rich, he started wondering whether he could live forever.

He decided to go from country to country until he would find a place where people don't die.

He prepared for the trip, told his wife what he was intending, and set off on his journey.

In each country he visited, he asked if people die in that place.

If the answer was that they did, he would continue his journey.

One day, he reached a country where the people hadn't heard of death.

"How do you avoid overcrowding," the man asked, "if people don't die?"

"Now and again, we hear someone calling us. Whoever answers the call doesn't come back."

"And do the people see the person who comes to call?" he asked.

"Of course they do," he was told.

The man was surprised at the stupidity of these people, who go after the one calling them, when they know full well they won't come back.

He returned home, took his entire fortune, his wife and children, and set off to settle in this strange place where people don't die.

He had decided that he and his family members would never go after whoever was to call them.

After they settled in the new place, he taught his wife and his children not to go with whoever was to call them, so they would avoid death.

They set about living and a few years passed.

One day, as they were all at home having a good time, his wife shouted:

"I'm coming now! I'm coming now!" and she put on her coat.

Our man jumped up and restrained her.

"Have you forgotten what I have taught you?" he said. "Don't go or you will die."

"Can't you see someone is calling me? I am going to see what he wants and I will return straight away."

She kept trying to escape her husband's arms, to follow the one who was calling her.

Her husband overpowered her and locked all the exits to the house.

"Let me be, I'm not going anywhere," she said, when she saw that she could not escape.

Her husband, thinking she had come to her senses, loosened the security measures he had put in place.

But as soon as he had done so, the woman threw herself at one of the doors he had unlocked and rushed out.

Her husband ran after her and grabbed her by the coat, telling her not to go, because she won't return.

She twisted herself out of his hold and the coat slipped off her shoulders.

Her husband was left holding her coat.

He was stunned as he watched her running as fast as she could.

"I'm coming, I'm coming," she kept shouting.

"If you're crazy and want to die, there's nothing I can do about it," he said. "I have told you how to avoid death, but if you want to die, it's your choice."

After she disappeared from view, our man returned home.

Days, weeks, months, years passed, without anything else happening to shatter the family's peace.

One day, as was his custom, our man was at the barber's having a shave.

The shop was full of people, and his beard was covered in foam.

"I'm not coming," he shouted, all of a sudden.

The barber and the other customers were stunned.

Our man started looking towards the door.

"Please understand once and for all, and leave me, because I'm not coming," he said.

Later he said again:

"Go away, if you want to escape without shame. I have already told you I am not coming."

It was as if someone was standing by the door, calling him continuously.

He kept getting more and more angry that he wasn't being left in peace.

In the end, he jumped and took the knife out of the barber's hand.

"Come here," he said, "so I show you what happens if you keep bothering me."

And he ran out the door in great haste, chasing the one who kept calling him, and whom nobody else could see.

The barber started running after him, to get his knife back.

The man ran, the barber after him, until they got to an area just outside the town.

The man fell into a precipice and never came back out, the same as all the others who had been called.

The barber returned to his shop, accepting the loss of his knife.

He told everyone what had happened.

Messages were sent throughout the country, telling everyone about that precipice.

Until then, nobody had been able to figure out what happened to the people who were being called.

But when a crowd gathered to search for the precipice, they couldn't find it.

All they found was a valley, which seemed to have been there since the beginning of time.

From then on, people started dying in that place too, as they do everywhere else.

TRANSLATOR'S NOTE (DEATH'S CALL)

I absolutely loved translating this little gem of a story.

It is one of the many unexpected delights in Petre Ispirescu's collection of tales.

This premise, of someone trying to find a place where there is no death, may be particularly enticing for fantasy or sci fi writers looking for their next big idea.

The original title is *Glasul Mortii*, which translates as 'Death's Voice' or 'The Voice of Death'.

If you enjoyed reading this brief story about a character struggling to come to terms with his own mortality, I recommend the longer and more well-rounded *Youth Everlasting*, which is the headline story in *Youth Everlasting and Other Romanian Fairy Tales.*

You may also enjoy reading a translation of Mihai Eminescu's extraordinary poem *Luceafarul.*

That poem explores the issue of mortality from the point of view of the Morning Star, Hyperion, who is immortal and wishes to give up his immortality for love.

I would like to ask you for a small favor.

Reviews are the best way to spread the word about this book.

If you have enjoyed reading this book, it would mean a lot to me if you could leave a review.

Even if you only write a sentence or two, it will help. Thank you!

ABOUT THE AUTHOR

Petre Ispirescu was born in 1830 in Bucharest, where he lived most of his life. He grew up around folk stories, and was greatly inspired by them.

His parents wanted him to become a priest, a career path that required him to start training since childhood.

But at age 14, Ispirescu dropped out of his priest training and took up an apprenticeship at a publishing house.

He was a hard worker and quickly rose through the ranks.

Eventually, he was able to publish his own projects, which is how his collection of fairy tales came about.

He started publishing fairy tales as early as 1862 and continued publishing them over the following two decades.

Sadly, Petre Ispirescu died from a stroke at age 57.

Yet a few of the fairy tales he collected and published are still part of the Romanian literature curriculum to this day.

ABOUT THE TRANSLATOR

Alexa J Ispas grew up in Romania and moved to Scotland at age 18.

She holds a PhD in psychology from the University of Edinburgh.

Her frequent visits to the Scottish Storytelling Centre inspired her to delve into her Romanian story heritage.

These explorations led her to discover old, forgotten Romanian gems that give us a glimpse into a way of life different from our own.

You can find more of Alexa's translations of old Romanian stories at www.storybothy.com

GET A FREE STORY

Jack the Pimple

Can the ugliest boy in the village marry the beautiful princess?

Read this charming story from 19th century Romania, collected by Petre Ispirescu and translated into English by Alexa J Ispas.

Download for free when you sign up to the newsletter at

www.storybothy.com/newsletter

CPSIA information can be obtained
at www.ICGtesting.com
Printed in the USA
LVHW091606040921
696958LV00019B/362